SCIENCE IN A BAG

Discovery Experiences Using Resealable Bags

Esther Egley

Fearon Teacher Aids
An imprint of Paramount Supplemental Education

DEDICATION

This resource book is dedicated to Elementary Education preservice students at Mississippi State University and to the educators who shared their ideas and enthusiasm for teaching.

Executive Editor: Carolea Williams
Editor: Ema Arcellana
Cover Photography: Fred Stimson
Inside Illustration: Martha Weston
Cover and Inside Design: Dianne Platner

ISBN 0-86653-884-4

Printed in the United States of America
1.9 8 7 6 5 4 3 2 1

TABLE OF CONTENTS

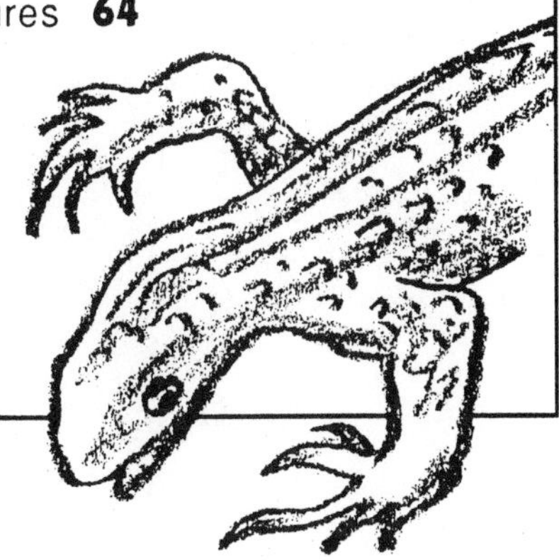

ACKNOWLEDGMENTS

It all started in 1990 when my students and I, in an Elementary Education class at Mississippi State University, started brainstorming ideas on how to get students closer to their learning despite the many problems that plagued our classrooms. One idea that evolved from that discussion used a resealable plastic bag. Within a few days, we had developed a concept complete with a multitude of activities. Since that time, I have shared the original ideas with teachers in workshops throughout the United States and have thus been given even more ideas to add. I would like to express my sincere appreciation to all of the teachers who freely shared their own ideas for this publication. And, I'd also like to thank all of the educators who simply shared with me through this project their enthusiasm for teaching. Many thanks to you all!

Anita Bailey
Amy Baker
Anndra Hill Barrett
Pamela Barr
Debra Bennett
Rita Bernard
Jarma Bridges
Diane Campbell
Jodi Causey
Becky Chancellor
Angela Clark
Valeri Crosby
Libby Cunningham
Louise Davis
Cindy Ford
Cathy Grace
Cathy Gregory
Marsha Guiss
Pat Hall
Andrew Howard
Lisa Kirk
Anita McConnell
Deborah Milligan
Bonnie Mizell
Marla Osband
Claudia Parra
Ginger Robertson
Margo Rushin
Shirley Schiff
Barbara Singleton
Elizabeth Sumner
Ita Thompson
Margaret Tribble
Clara Ware
Amy Whitley
Sammie Williams
Julie Wilson

INTRODUCTION

How many times have you said, "I would use more hands-on experiences, especially in the area of science, if I had more space, money, materials, equipment, or time." While your resources may be limited and your time at a premium, it is possible to offer your children quality hands-on experiences using simple, readily-available materials. *Science in a Bag* offers exciting discovery experiences using one of the most common and easy-to-find resources—resealable bags.

One of the keys to successful hands-on science experiences is good organization. With careful planning, you can eliminate all of the obstacles that prevent you from using hands-on activities more frequently. Here are some tips to help you and your students be successful as you enjoy the activities in this resource.

STAYING ORGANIZED

- Read each activity completely before beginning.
- Allow time to gather the needed materials. Many items can be supplied by parents.
- Set aside a table or countertop for supplies.
- Designate certain children to gather materials for a group or be a clean-up monitor.
- Recruit upper-class students or parent volunteers to assist.
- Set aside an area in your room to store materials according to topic or in alphabetical order.
- Staple resealable bags to bulletin boards, tape them to walls, or hang them on a clothesline to save space.

EFFECTIVE CLEANUP

- Make sure students know the procedures for cleanup before the lesson begins.
- Cover work areas with newspaper whenever possible.
- Have trash bags near every work area. The clean-up monitors can empty the bags into the classroom trash can at the end of the investigation.
- Place baby wipes and paper towels at each station in order to avoid congestion at the sink.

SAFETY PRECAUTIONS

- Check with parents at the beginning of the year to be aware of any allergies your children may have.
- Use water-based inks and markers instead of solvent-based inks and markers.
- Encourage children to wash their hands with soap and water when necessary.
- Investigations requiring heat should be closely supervised or performed only by the teacher.
- Warn children against placing materials in their mouths.

One major goal of early childhood educators is to help children build a foundation that will set the stage for all future learning. As you use the activities in this resource, you will be building such a foundation by:

- giving children opportunities to interact with their environment
- involving children in activities that engage all of their senses
- allowing children time and freedom to make their own discoveries
- developing process skills and critical thinking

Observing
Classifying
Measuring
Hypothesizing
Predicting
Describing
Drawing Conclusions
Asking Questions
Inferring
Formulating Problems
Designing Investigations

Clear away your obstacles, use the resources that surround you, and help children discover the excitement of learning through fun and unique hands-on experiences.

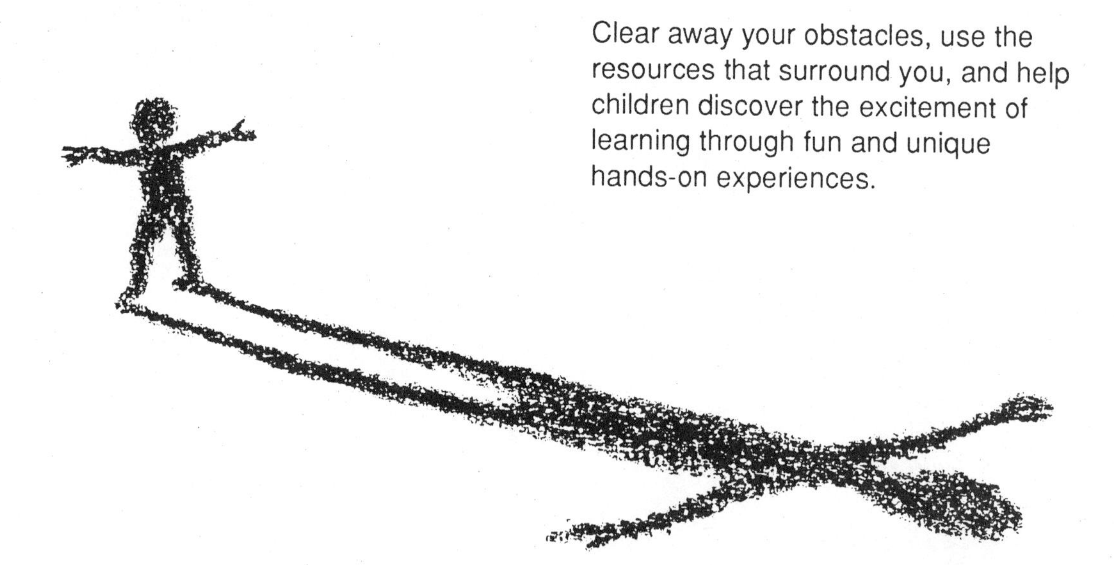

WRINKLED RAISINS

Children will discuss various conditions necessary to turn grapes to raisins and then test their ideas.

MATERIALS

sandwich-size resealable bags

raisins

magnifying glasses

grapes

paper

pencils, crayons, markers

Investigation

1. Have pairs of children observe and examine a raisin and a grape using a magnifying glass.
2. Ask children to compare and contrast the two types of food.
3. After explaining to children that raisins are made from grapes, give each child several grapes sealed in a bag.
4. Challenge children to design an experiment (based on what they discovered during their observations) that will change their grapes into raisins. What conditions will be necessary? How long will it take?
5. Encourage children to test their ideas and record their results.

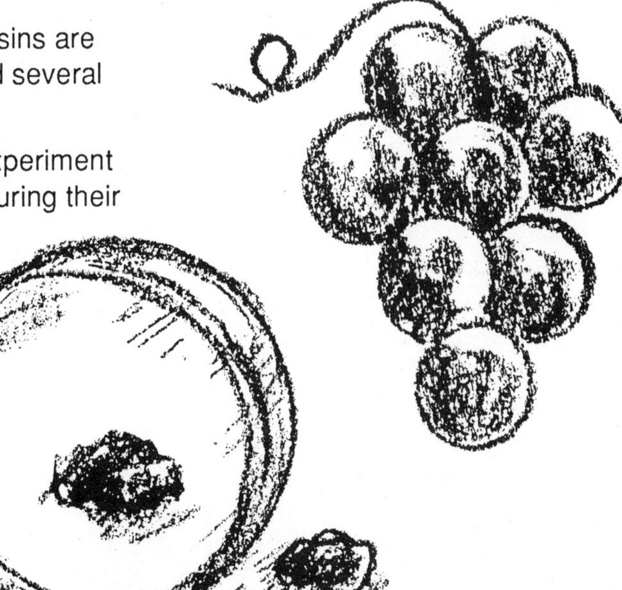

EXTENSIONS

- Invite children to make grape juice.
- Discuss ways to make juice or dried products from other fruits, such as apples, strawberries, or apricots.

MAKING MEATLOAF

Children will predict how the ingredients in meatloaf will smell, feel, and look before and after baking.

MATERIALS

gallon-size resealable bag

2 lbs. ground beef

2 eggs

1/4 cup mustard

1/2 cup catsup

1/2 tsp. salt

1/2 tsp. pepper

1 cup uncooked oats

loaf pan

Investigation

1. Invite children to help measure and combine the meatloaf ingredients in the large resealabe bag.
2. Ask children to smell and carefully observe each ingredient as it is added. How do the ingredients look different when they are all mixed together?
3. Seal the bag securely and invite children to take turns massaging and manipuiating the bag until the ingredients are thoroughly mixed. How does the bag feel?
4. Empty the mixture into a loaf pan and bake at 350° F for about 40 minutes.
5. Ask children how the cooked meatloaf and the ingredients that went into the bag are alike or different.

EXTENSIONS

- Use other recipes, such as cookies and bread.
- Invite children to create individual hamburger patties using smaller bags and ingredient proportions. Have a class barbecue.

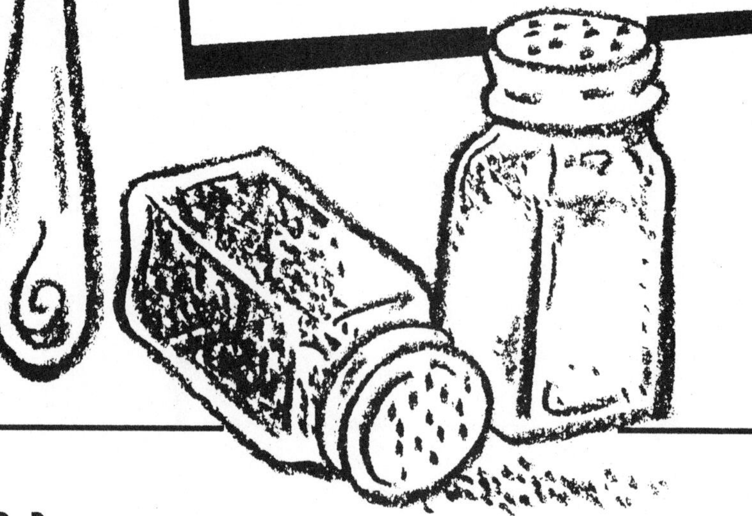

ICE CREAM FREEZE

Children will combine ingredients and use an ice shaker-bag to make homemade ice cream.

MATERIALS

- gallon-size resealable bags
- quart-size resealable bags
- 4 eggs (beaten)
- 2 cups sugar
- 4 cups half & half
- 1 Tbsp. vanilla
- 1 tsp. table salt
- 3 quarts milk
- crushed ice
- rock salt
- gallon-size plastic container
- small paper cups
- plastic spoons
- hand towels

Investigation

1. Invite children to help measure and combine eggs, sugar, half & half, vanilla, table salt, and milk in the large plastic container.
2. Have children take turns stirring until the ingredients are well blended.
3. Measure about one cup of the ice cream mixture into a quart-size resealable bag for each pair of children. Seal the bags securely.
4. Help each pair of children fill a gallon-size resealable bag half full of ice and add 1/2 cup of rock salt.
5. Have children place their sealed bags of ice cream into the bags of ice and seal securely.
6. Students can take turns kneading the bags until the ice cream mixture begins to thicken. (Wrap the bags in hand towels if they become too cold to handle.)
7. Add more rock salt if needed to speed the freezing process.
8. Carefully remove the frozen ice cream from the bag and place it in paper cups to enjoy.

EXTENSIONS

- Invite children to bring toppings to create ice cream sundaes.
- Try the same method to make frozen juice ices.

MUFFIN MAKERS

Children will discover that ingredients can change forms and textures while preparing a batch of muffins.

MATERIALS

large resealable bag

muffin mix

muffin pans

measuring utensils

oven

scissors

Investigation

1. Empty the muffin mix into the bag and invite children to help measure and add the remaining ingredients listed on the muffin box.
2. Seal the bag securely and invite students to mix the ingredients by massaging the bag. How do the ingredients look different now than when they were first placed in the bag?
3. Cut open one lower corner of the bag.
4. Encourage students to take turns squeezing the mixture out of the bag into the muffin pans.
5. Bake as directed. How have the ingredients we placed in the bag changed? Do they look different? Feel different? Taste different? Why?

EXTENSIONS

- Use recipes, such as cake and brownie mixes.
- Invite children to create their own recipes and predict how the ingredients will change forms and textures.

NUTRITIOUS SNACKS

Children will create their own snack bags and consider the nutritional value of the contents.

Investigation

1. Discuss healthy foods, such as foods low in sugar, low in salt, and high in fiber.
2. Display the bowls of food and discuss why each is or is not nutritious.
3. Invite each student to select ingredients for his or her own nutritious snack bag by placing a small scoop of each selection in a resealable bag.
4. Encourage children to share what they chose for their snack bags.

quart-size resealable bags

scoops (approximately 1/4 cup in size)

various snack foods in bowls (pretzels, oat cereal, raisins, cereal fruit squares, peanuts, chocolate chips)

EXTENSIONS

- Students can place pictures of foods in their bags instead of the real foods.
- Ask students to name other snacks they enjoy and place them in two groups—nutritious or non-nutritious.

SALAD BUFFET

Children will learn about the importance of vegetables in their diet while preparing a salad.

Investigation

1. Ask children to help wash and prepare the vegetables.
2. Place each vegetable in a separate unsealed quart-size bag on a table buffet style.
3. Place a serving spoon with each bag.
4. Give each child a sandwich-size bag and invite children to walk down the buffet and create salads in their bags.
5. After children have selected their ingredients, help them seal the bags and toss the salads.
6. As children add salad dressing and enjoy their salads, remind them that the foods they eat provide them with the energy they need.

MATERIALS

sandwich-size resealable bags

quart-size resealable bags

plastic forks

lettuce

carrots

tomatoes

celery

bell peppers

broccoli

salad dressing

serving spoons

EXTENSIONS

- Instead of using real salad ingredients, students may make salads in their bags using pictures they cut from magazines or draw themselves.
- Group and graph the salads in as many ways as possible. What ingredients did no one choose? What combination of ingredients was the most popular? What ingredients did everybody choose?

BREAD IN A BAG

Children will practice the skill of measuring while preparing a bread recipe.

large resealable bag

2 cups all-purpose flour

1 package rapid rise yeast

3 Tbsp. sugar

3 Tbsp. nonfat dry milk

1 tsp. salt

1 cup hot water

3 Tbsp. vegetable oil

1 cup whole wheat flour

measuring utensils

glass loaf pans

oven

bowls

Investigation

1. Help children measure and place the dry ingredients (1 cup all-purpose flour, yeast, sugar, nonfat dry milk, and salt) in the large bag.
2. Squeeze out the air, seal the bag securely, and have children shake the bag to blend the ingredients.
3. Open the bag and carefully add the hot water and oil to the dry ingredients.
4. Reseal the bag and ask children to knead the bag to mix the ingredients. (Be sure the bag is not too hot for children to handle.)
5. Add the whole wheat flour, reseal the bag, and invite children to continue kneading and massaging the bag.
6. Invite students to gradually add enough of the remaining all-purpose flour to make a stiff dough that pulls away from the bag.
7. Remove the dough from the bag and invite children to take turns kneading it on a floured surface for 2-4 minutes.
8. Cover the dough and allow it to rise for 10 minutes. What do you think will happen to the dough if we don't touch it for 10 minutes? Why? What is yeast? What other foods besides bread have yeast in them?
9. Place the dough in an oiled loaf pan and let it rise for 20 minutes.
10. Bake at 375° F for 25 minutes.

EXTENSIONS

- Discuss nutrition or chemical reactions.
- Use other recipes, such as sugar cookies or gelatin.

More M&M's

Children will estimate, count, and group the M&M's in a package.

Materials

sandwich-size resealable bags

small packages of M&M's

paper

pencils, markers, or crayons

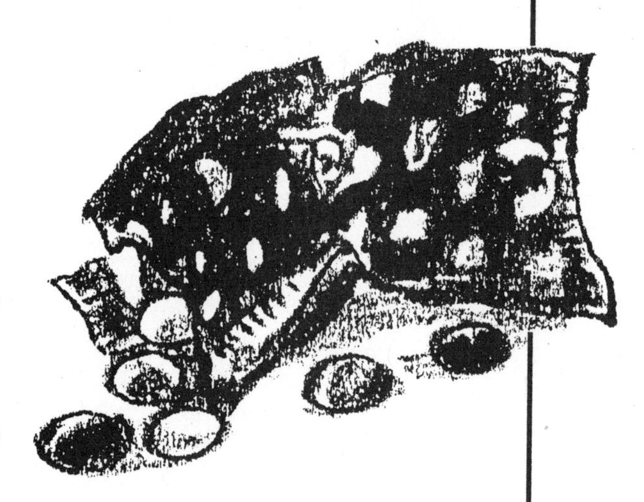

Investigation

1. Empty each package of M&M's into a resealable bag. Remove as much air as possible from the bags and seal them securely.
2. Give one bag of M&M's to each pair of children.
3. Invite children to estimate and record the number of M&M's they think are in their bags.
4. Have children count and record the actual number of M&M's in their bags.
5. Discuss the accuracy of children's predictions and the methods they used to estimate.
6. Invite children to group their M&M's by color and count the number in each color group.
7. Have children add the total of each color group together and compare that total with their record of the total number of M&M's in the bag.

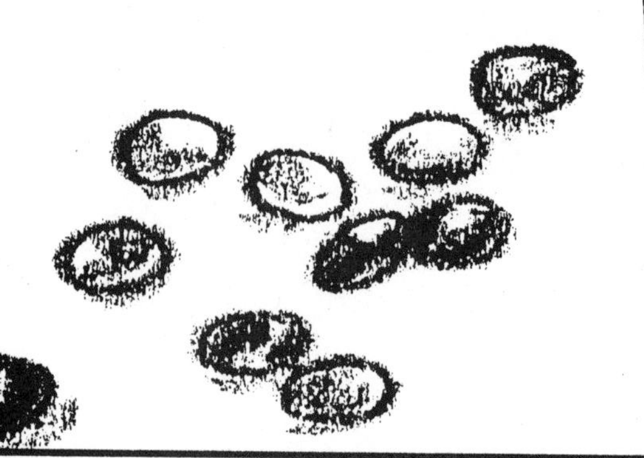

Extensions

- Add each pair's total for each M&M color together to get class totals for each candy color. Graph the results.
- Graph children's color preferences.
- Ask children math-related questions about their candies. How many green and red M&M's do you have altogether? Which color do you have the least of? How many M&M's would you have in your bag if you took out all of the brown ones?

SANDWICH SURVEY

In this activity, students make paper sandwiches, classify their sandwiches according to type of bread, and graph their findings.

MATERIALS

sandwich-size resealable bags

construction paper

pencils, markers, or crayons

scissors

chart or butcher paper

push pins or tape

Investigation

1. Invite children to recreate their favorite sandwiches by cutting ingredients, such as bologna, bread, mustard, and tomatoes, from construction paper.
2. Have each student place his or her paper sandwich in a resealable bag.
3. Ask children to describe their sandwiches so that others can guess what kind they are.
4. Graph the sandwiches according to types of bread by inviting children to tape or tack their bagged sandwiches on a large graph.
5. Encourage the class to summarize and interpret the graph.
6. Ask children what other groups the sandwiches could be sorted into. Which group would have the most sandwiches? The least?

EXTENSIONS

- Have a class picnic and provide ingredients for children to make real sandwiches.
- Invite children to recreate other favorites besides food, such as toys, books, or clothes. Graph according to various criteria.

SOAK IT UP

Children will observe that some objects soak up water when immersed and others do not.

Investigation

1. Invite children to compare what would happen if they stood in the rain wearing a raincoat and if they stood in the rain not wearing a raincoat.
2. Show the objects to the children and invite them to predict and record which objects will soak up water when immersed.
3. Give each pair of children a resealable bag filled 1/2 full of water.
4. Encourage children to test their predictions and record their findings.
5. Encourage children to compare their predictions with their results.

MATERIALS

large resealable bags

water

several small porous objects (dry sponge, paper towel, cottonball)

several small nonporous objects (granite rock, marble, aluminum foil)

paper

pencils, markers, or crayons

EXTENSIONS

- Encourage children to bring objects from home to test or to conduct some tests at home and report on the results.
- Challenge children to apply their conclusions from the experiment to create the perfect foul-weather gear.

SINK OR FLOAT

Children will investigate the buoyancy of several objects.

MATERIALS

quart-size resealable bags

water

objects (cork, Styrofoam pieces, ping-pong ball, wooden block, pebble, marble, iron bolt, nail)

chart paper

markers

Investigation

1. Discuss with children the meaning of the words *sink* and *float*.
2. Display each object and ask children to predict whether, when placed in water, the object will sink or float. Do you think the pebble will sink or float? How can we find out?
3. Record predictions on chart paper.
4. Place the items one at a time in a bag that is filled 1/3 full of water. Trap the air inside and seal.
5. Invite children to carefully observe.
6. Have children compare their predictions and results. Discuss why some objects float while others sink.

EXTENSIONS

- Give each child an opportunity to have a personal sink or float bag to test the buoyancy of objects.
- Use other liquids, such as very salty water, fruit juice, tea, or cola instead of water.

OIL AND WATER

Children will discover that water and oil do not mix and then apply what they have learned to a real-life situation.

MATERIALS

sandwich-size resealable bags

water

blue food coloring

mineral oil

paper

pencils, markers, or crayons

Investigation

1. Mix water and food coloring in a large container.
2. Help each child fill a bag with three parts blue water and one part oil.
3. Remove as much air from the bags as possible and seal securely.
4. Encourage children to observe and record what the water and oil mixture looks like and how it moves when they manipulate the bags.
5. Encourage children to record their observations.
6. Lead children in a discussion about what they discovered about water and oil. Invite them to share what they think would happen if oil spilled in the oceans, including how it would affect animals and how it could be cleaned up.

EXTENSIONS

- Discuss the difference in density between water and oil.
- Encourage children to combine two other liquids to perform the same experiment.

DISSOLVING DELIGHTS

Children will test the solubility of objects in water.

Investigation

1. Place 1/2 cup of each of the first thirteen substances in the materials list in a separate resealable bag.
2. Show children the bags one at a time and encourage them to predict which are water soluble. Record their predictions on chart paper.
3. Test and record the solubility of each item by adding water to each bag. Seal the bags securely and invite children to manipulate them.
4. Invite children to discuss the results.

EXTENSIONS

- Invite children to bring substances from home to use in the activity.
- Ask children to categorize the ingredients in the bags (before water is added). Which of the substances could be found in the kitchen, bathroom, bedroom?
- Challenge children to identify the dry substances by using only their sense of touch.

MATERIALS

popped popcorn

laundry detergent

pancake mix

baby powder

salt

shaving cream

grape juice

instant tea

granola cereal

lotion

uncooked rice

sugar cubes

graham crackers

sandwich-size resealable bags

chart paper

water

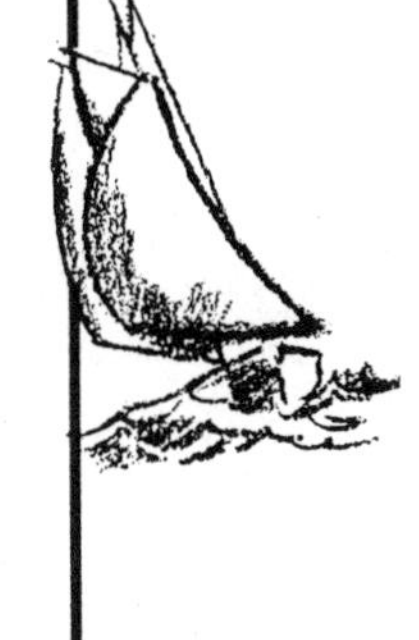

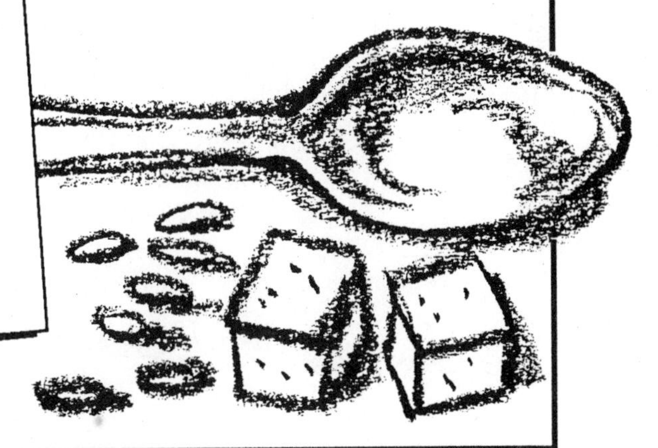

PLOP, PLIP, FUZZ, FIZZ

Children will observe the chemical reaction that occurs when antacid tablets are placed in water.

sandwich-size resealable bags

water

antacid tablets

1. Encourage children to predict what will happen when antacid tablets are added to water.
2. Help each pair of children pour 3/4 cup water into a bag and add two antacid tablets. Seal the bags quickly to trap the air inside.
3. Invite children to observe the chemical reaction. Make sure they listen to the reaction and watch the sides of the bag also.
4. Lead a discussion about what happened and why, including the production of carbon dioxide gas.

EXTENSIONS

- Use other liquids, such as hot water, cold water, or milk.
- Investigate the difference in the reaction if different amounts of antacid tablets are used in the same amount of water.

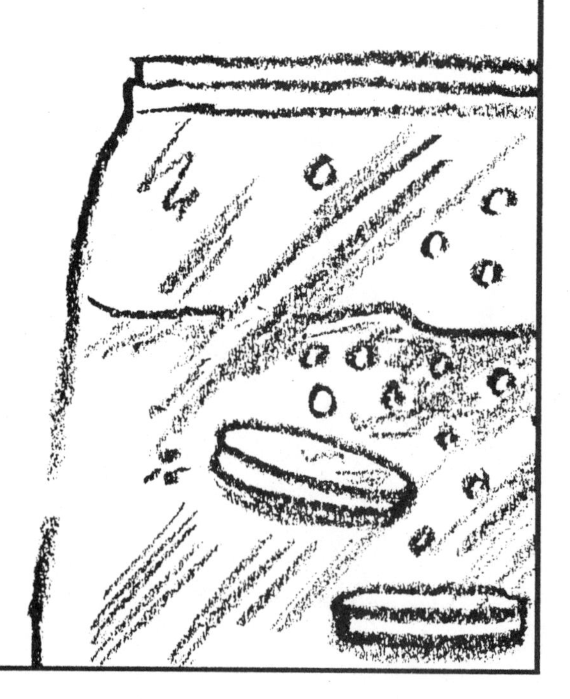

SPECKLED WATER

Children will explore movement by observing crayon shavings in water.

MATERIALS

quart-size resealable bags

water

crayons

child safety scissors

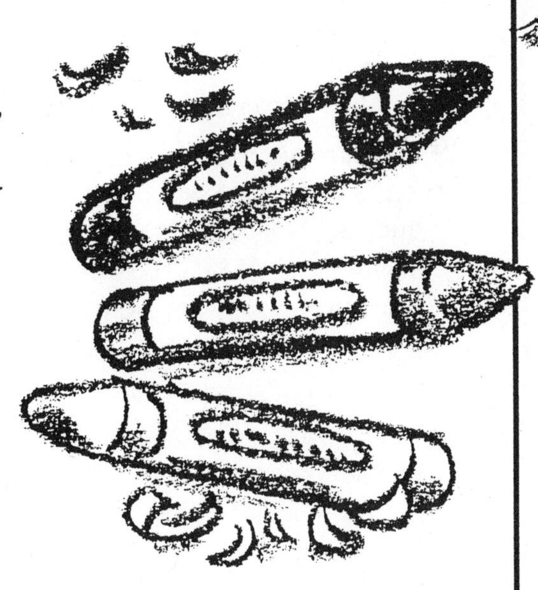

Investigation

1. Help children make crayon shavings by scraping crayons with the blade of child safety scissors under close adult supervision. Talk with children about making long shavings, short shavings, and using a variety of colors.
2. Help each child fill a resealable bag with water and add his or her crayon shavings. Release as much air from the bags as possible before sealing securely.
3. Encourage children to shake the bags of speckled water and observe the movement. How many different ways can you make the water or shavings move?
4. Have children place the bags on their desks and observe the speckled water settle. What happens to the shavings when the water is no longer moving?
5. After an appropriate amount of time, invite students to share their observations.

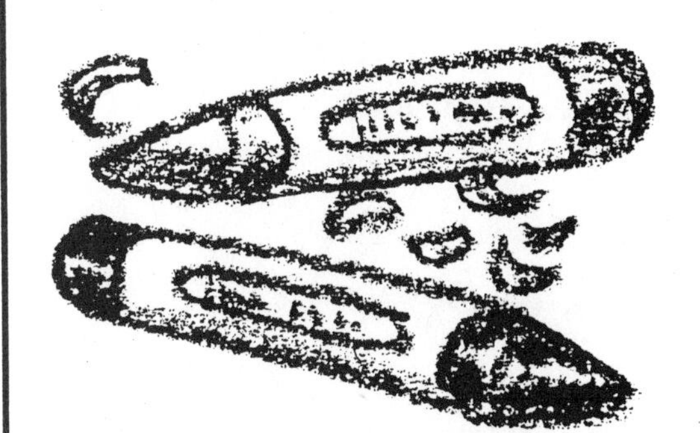

EXTENSIONS

- Add glitter to a resealable bag. Shine a light on the bag, shake it, and observe.
- Place other objects in the water, such as candle wax shavings and small pieces of a wax-coated cardboard milk carton. Invite children to suggest other things they would like to try adding to the water.

HOT OR COLD

Children will investigate the characteristics of hot and cold by feeling and describing temperatures of water.

Investigation

1. Invite children to list things that are warm, hot, or cold. Record their ideas on chart paper with words or pictures.
2. Prepare one bag of hot water, one bag of warm water, and one bag of cold water for each small group of children. Label each bag with a different colored label.
3. Have children feel the outside of the bag containing warm water and describe how the bag feels.
4. Have children feel the outside of the bag containing hot water and then immediately feel the warm water. (The warm water should now feel cold.)
5. Have children feel the outside of the bag containing cold water and then immediately feel the warm water. (The warm water should now feel warm.)
6. Invite children to share their thoughts. Challenge children to explain why the warm water felt warm after feeling the cold water and cold after the feeling the hot water.

MATERIALS

resealable bags

cold water

warm water

comfortably hot water

paper towels

colored labels

EXTENSIONS

- **Have children measure and record the temperature of each bag of water.**
- **Experiment using other liquids, such as soda or fruit juice.**

ICE SCULPTURES

Children will observe and discuss the formation of ice sculptures.

MATERIALS

gallon-size resealable bag

quart-size resealable bags

salt

food coloring

water

scissors

large plastic tub

freezer

Investigation

1. Fill the gallon-size resealable bag with water and freeze it.
2. When the water is frozen, run water over the bag to loosen it. Remove the ice from the bag and place it in a large tub.
3. Help each child mix 1/4 cup warm water, 15 drops of food coloring, and 3/4 cup of salt in a quart-size resealable bag before sealing the bag securely.
4. Demonstrate how to make an ice cavern by holding one of the bags of salt water over the ice in the tub at an angle so that all the liquid gathers in one corner of the bag. Cut a small hole at the tip of the bag so the liquid squirts out onto the ice as you squeeze the bag. (Avoid letting too much of the liquid pile up in one area. If this happens, rinse the ice with water.)
5. Invite children to take turns squirting the salt solution onto the ice to make ice cavern formations. How long will the ice stay frozen? What will affect this? Why?

EXTENSIONS

- Ask children what might happen if other liquids were squirted onto the ice. Test children's ideas.
- Challenge children to create other ways to make ice sculptures.

MELTING RACE

Children will create ways to melt an ice cube as quickly as possible.

MATERIALS

sandwich-size resealable bags

ice cubes

chart paper

markers

Investigation

1. Ask students to discuss what causes ice to melt. Record children's ideas on chart paper.
2. Place an ice cube in a sealed bag for each child.
3. Invite children to test their ideas about what makes ice melt by trying to melt their ice cubes as quickly as possible. Does it matter where you place your ice cube in the classroom? Does temperature affect the melting rate?

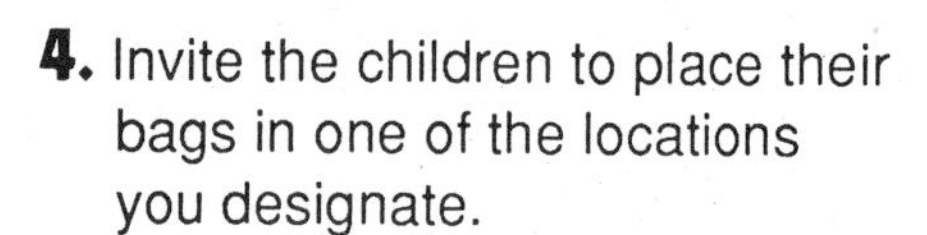

4. Invite the children to place their bags in one of the locations you designate.
5. After 15 minutes, have children compare their ice cubes (or what is left of them) and discuss what experiments they tried. What did you discover? What would you do differently next time?

EXTENSIONS

- Experiment using different shapes or amounts of ice.
- Experiment with ice made from different types of water, such as distilled, hard, soft, salt, pond, or bottled.
- Students may time and record how long it takes to melt the ice cubes completely.
- Encourage children to notice and discuss the condensation that forms on the outside of the bags.
- Read *Changes, Changes* by Pat Hutchins.

SHADOWS AND SHAPES

Children will explore light and shadows.

MATERIALS

resealable bags

water

food coloring

objects (buttons, Styrofoam pieces, small foam/sponge shapes, leaf, waxed cardboard shapes)

overhead projector

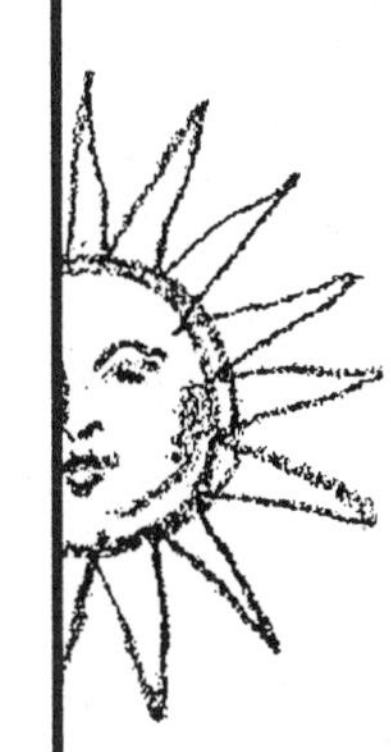

Investigation

1. Fill several resealable bags with colored water.
2. Place one or more objects in each bag.
3. Squeeze out as much air as possible from the bags and seal securely.
4. Encourage children to predict what will happen when you place each bag on the overhead projector. Will light travel through water, paper, or plastic? Will you see a shadow? Why?
5. Dim the classroom lights and place one bag at a time flat on an overhead projector to project the images on the wall. (Do not leave the resealable bag on the overhead projector too long.)
6. Encourage the class to discuss what they observe, such as why shadows are cast and why light travels through colored water.
7. Discuss how light travels, refracts, and is reflected.

EXTENSIONS

- Add glitter to one of the resealable bags before experimenting.
- Carefully add drops of food coloring to the bag immediately before you seal it and place it on the overhead projector. Watch the colors mix on the wall.

REFLECTING LIGHT

Children will evaluate the ability of different materials to reflect light.

MATERIALS

quart-size resealable bags

flashlight

foil

plastic wrap

black construction paper

scissors

paper

pencils, markers, or crayons

Investigation

1. Cut the construction paper, foil, and plastic wrap into pieces that will fit inside the bags.
2. Place the paper, foil, and plastic wrap into separate bags.
3. Encourage children to predict and record which materials will reflect the most or least light.
4. Invite children to shine the flashlight beam on each surface and record their observations.
5. Encourage children to share and compare the results and their predictions.

EXTENSIONS

- Experiment using other materials.
- Compare and contrast the ability of the materials to reflect light with the ability to absorb heat.

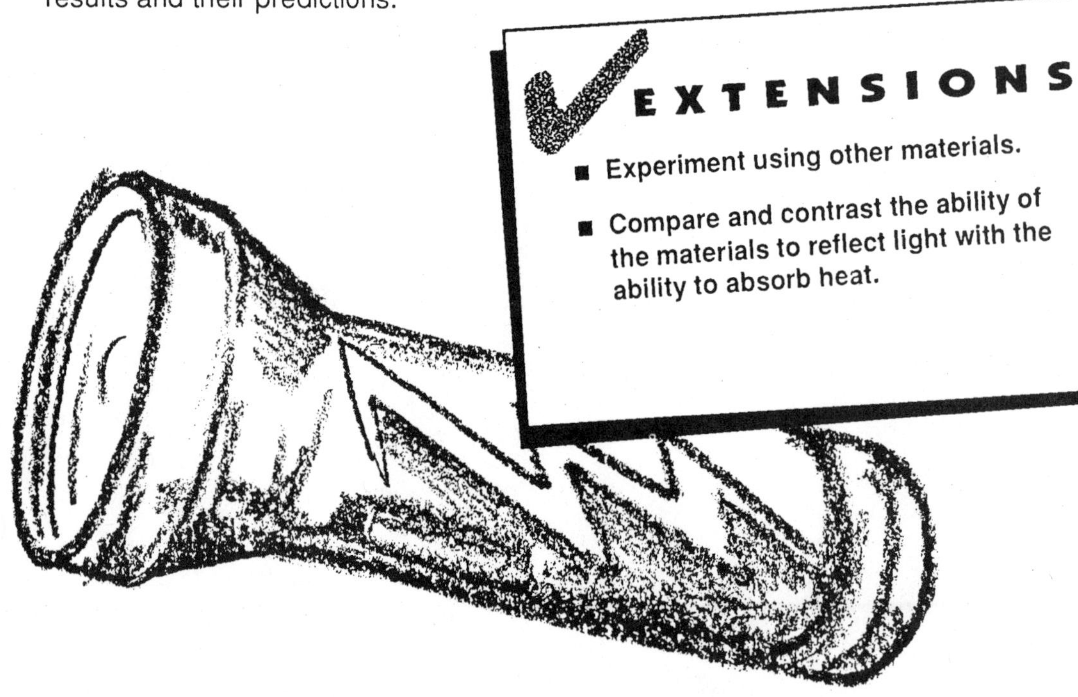

COLORED PAPER

Children will study the capillary action of water by observing colored water travel through paper.

MATERIALS

quart-size resealable bags

coffee filters (or paper towels)

water

food coloring

stapler

tape

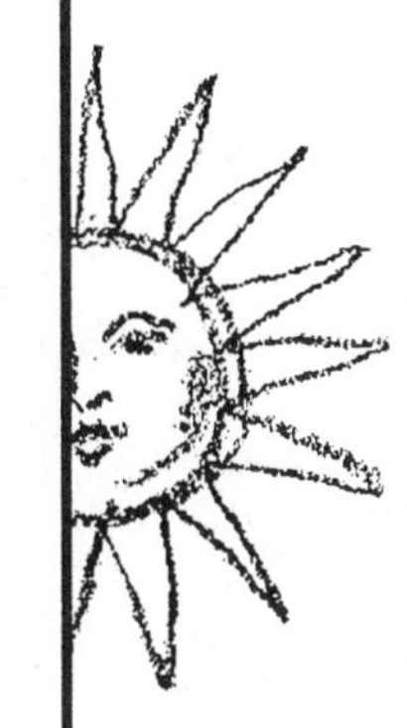

Investigation

1. Staple one resealable bag per child to a bulletin board and add about 1/4 cup water and a few drops of food coloring to each bag. Be sure the bags are low enough so that children can easily reach them.
2. Help each child fold a coffee filter so that the center of the filter becomes the point of a cone.
3. Invite children to predict what will happen when coffee filters are placed in the colored water.
4. Help children tape the coffee filters in their resealable bags so that only the tip of the point is touching the colored water.
5. Encourage children to observe the set up and record their observations over the next two days.
6. Invite children to share and record their observations.

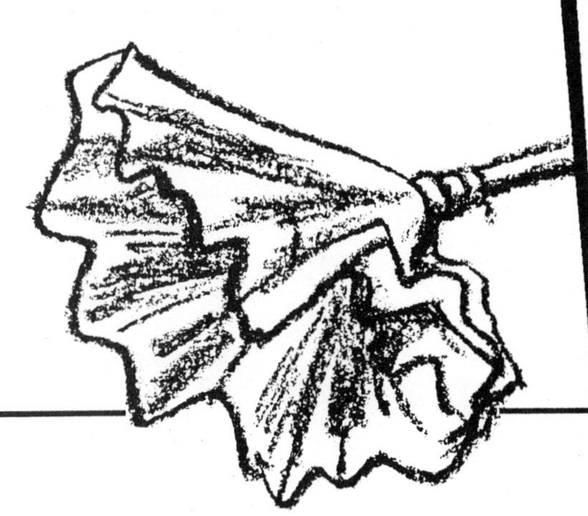

EXTENSIONS

- Children can form their colored coffee filters into flowers. Use pipe cleaners to hold the flowers together and create stems.
- Invite children to repeat the experiment using different types of paper or liquids.

TOUCH AND THINK

Children will investigate mixing and separating colors in a solution of water, oil, and corn starch.

MATERIALS

large resealable freezer bag

5 Tbsp. corn starch

1/2 cup water

1/2 cup oil

green and blue food coloring (2 drops each)

masking tape

paper

pencils, markers, or crayons

Investigation

1. Mix the corn starch, water, and food coloring in a bag and then add the oil.
2. Close the bag securely and tape the seal for extra protection.
3. Lay the bag flat on a table in the middle of the room so all students can gather around to view the investigation.
4. Invite the class to predict what will happen if they manipulate the bag. How can you make the liquid move? What colors do you see? How might this activity be different if we didn't use oil?
5. Encourage children to press the contents of the bag with their fingers and watch the colors mix.
6. Invite children to record their observations with pictures or words.
7. Ask the class to share their observations and draw some conclusions.

EXTENSIONS

- Make several "touch and think" bags using different color combinations.
- Prepare a bag without the oil to see if the students discover a difference.

STAINED GLASS

Children will observe how different colors of paint mix to form new colors.

MATERIALS

quart-size resealable bags

several colors of paint

Investigation

1. Place a total of 5 teaspoons of paint inside each resealable bag. Be sure to vary the colors from bag to bag.
2. Release as much air as possible from the bags and seal securely.
3. Invite children to manipulate and massage the bags to mix the colors. Encourage children to predict what will happen to the colors in each bag before they begin.
4. Encourage children to illustrate or describe the new colors they create. What colors did you make? What colors can you see in your bag? What will happen when the paint dries in your bag?
5. Invite children to hang the bags up in the window after the paint has dried to make stained glass windows.

EXTENSIONS

- Children can draw a stained glass window design on paper and then try to duplicate it using paint and a resealable bag.
- Give students recipe cards describing a paint mixing equation, such as 1 spoon green + 1 spoon blue = ______. Invite children to solve the equation with a prediction and then test their results.

BUBBLE PRISMS

Children will create prisms using a solution of dish washing soap, water, and glycerin and then observe the colors of the spectrum created by the prism.

MATERIALS

quart-size resealable bags

large bowl

1 quart water

4 Tbsp. liquid dish washing soap

4 Tbsp. glycerin

paper

markers or crayons

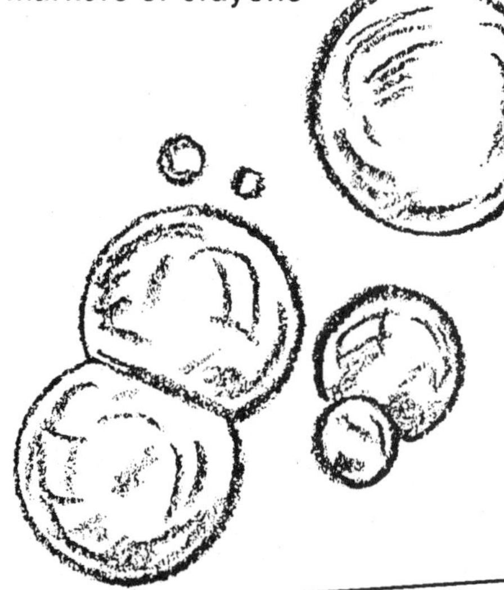

Investigation

1. Mix the water, dish washing soap, and glycerin in a large bowl.
2. Help each child fill a resealable bag 1/4 full of the mixture and seal it securely. (Be sure to leave some air in the bags.)
3. Invite children to shake their bags and observe closely. What colors do you see?
4. Children can hold the bags up to artificial lights in the classroom or up to a sunny window. Why can you see colors in the bubbles? What colors make up the spectrum?
5. Invite students to share their observations. Discuss the colors of the spectrum, how they are created, and how the bubble bags act as prisms.

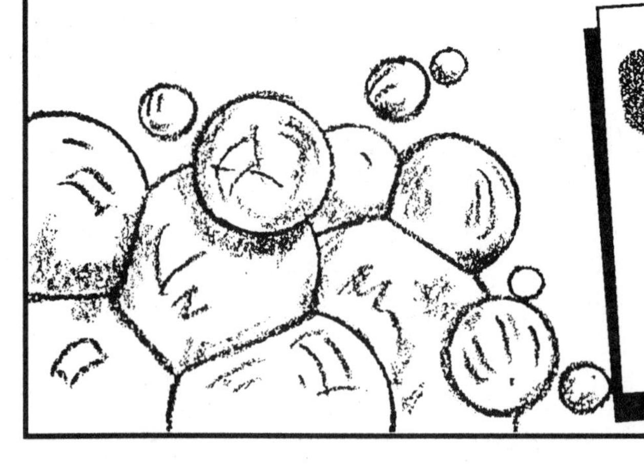

EXTENSIONS

- Experiment using different kinds of soap.
- Investigate using different colors of lights.

COLOR DETECTIVES

Children will use paper chromatography to separate the pigments in pen ink.

quart-size resealable bags

coffee filters

non-permanent watercolor markers

water

scissors

tape

Investigation

1. Tape each child's resealable bag to a window or bulletin board and place 1/2 cup of water in each bag.
2. Cut large squares from the coffee filters.
3. Encourage children to predict what will happen when a piece of paper with a dot of ink on it is placed in water.
4. Hold up several colors of watercolor markers one at a time and ask children to guess what combination of colors each pen is made of.
5. Invite children to carefully cut the coffee filter squares into five strips without cutting the top edge.
6. Using markers, have children place a dot of ink on each section of the coffee filter about 1-1/2 inches from the bottom. They may use a different color of ink on each section.
7. Invite children to tape the coffee filter to the inside of their bags so that the lower edge of the coffee filter is barely touching the water. Carefully seal the bags.
8. Give children time to observe the colors separating.
9. After the investigation, invite children to share their findings. Discuss how pigments mix to form new colors.

EXTENSIONS

- Perform the activity using different kinds of paper and compare the results.
- Experiment with different types of markers.

FOAMING FUN

Children will study properties of shaving cream and experiment mixing colors in the shaving cream.

MATERIALS

quart-size resealable bags

shaving cream

food coloring

Investigation

1. Invite children to share their experiences with shaving cream, such as what it feels like, how it smells, and what it's used for.
2. Place a small portion of shaving cream in each child's bag.
3. Invite children to add two or more colors of food coloring to the shaving cream and then predict what color will be created when they mix the shaving cream and food coloring.
4. Help children seal the bags securely before they begin massaging them.
5. After an appropriate amount of time, discuss the students' findings and what colors mixed to form new colors.

EXTENSIONS

- Use other substances, such as pudding.
- Read *Purple, Green, and Yellow* by Robert Munsch.
- Record what colors mix to form new colors on chart paper.

HOT AND COLD COLORS

Children will investigate the ability of colors to absorb heat.

MATERIALS

resealable bags

various colors of construction paper, such as black, orange, and white

Investigation

1. Cut the construction paper into pieces that will fit into the bags and place one color of paper into each bag.
2. Place the bags in a warm location, such as a window sill, to absorb heat.
3. Show children the bags that have been left near a sunny window. Invite children to predict which color will feel the warmest.
4. Encourage children to feel each colored paper to test their predictions.
5. Invite children to share their observations. Challenge children to explain why some colors absorb more heat than others.

EXTENSIONS

- **Repeat the experiment using other materials, such as fabric, aluminum foil, or plastic.**
- **Line the bags with colored paper and place small jars of water in the bags. Children can feel which jar of water gets the warmest when placed near a sunny window.**

ANT FARM

Children will determine the types of food ants prefer.

large resealable bags

paper

shortening or lard

masking tape

scoop or large spoon

ant mound

food scraps (candy, bread, meat)

Investigation

1. Encourage children to think about ants—where have they seen ants and what kind of food ants like.
2. Place several cups of soil along with some ants inside several resealable bags. (Thoroughly grease the inside of the bags below the seals to prevent the ants from crawling out.)
3. Ask children to consider what types of food they would like to place in the bags. Place a piece of each food scrap in each bag and seal the bags securely. Tape the seal for added safety.
4. Staple the bags to a bulletin board so children can easily observe the ants.
5. After several days of observations, invite students to discuss what types of food the ants seemed to prefer and draw some conclusions about their food preferences.

EXTENSIONS

- Explore the effects of location (window sill, closet, high shelf) on the ants' food preferences.
- Do the same investigation using ants from different mounds.
- Investigate food preference of other insects.

POND LIFE

Children will observe organisms found in a pond or a stream.

Investigation

1. Cover the bottom inch or two of the bag with mud, gravel, or debris from the bottom of a stream or pond.
2. Pour the pond or stream water into the bag.
3. Add any small organisms, such as tadpoles or minnows, from the site to the resealable bag.
4. Encourage children to closely observe the bag. Invite them to smell the water.
5. Lead the class in a discussion about their observations. Encourage them to share what they think the organisms need to live.
6. After a couple of days, return the organisms to the original site or add them to the class aquarium.

MATERIALS

large resealable bag

mud, gravel, or debris from a pond or stream

small organisms from a pond or stream

6-8 cups of water from a pond or stream

EXTENSIONS

- Small groups of students may prepare their own bags to observe.
- If possible, take the class on a nature walk to a nearby stream to study.
- Students may illustrate their observations.

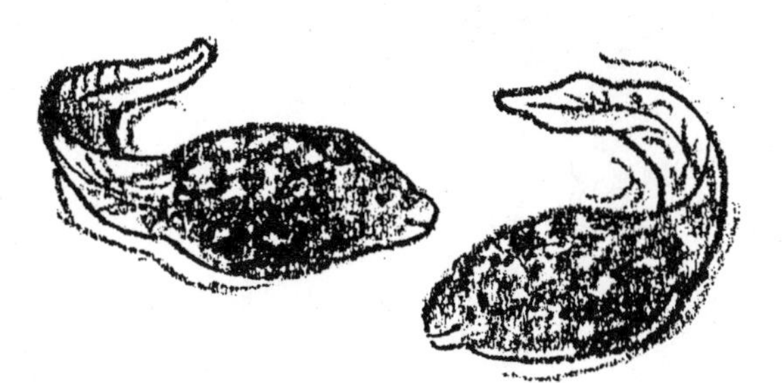

CRITTERS AND CREATURES

Children will observe and record the characteristics of a lizard.

MATERIALS

large resealable bag

magnifying glass

lizard (or other creature spontaneously discovered on the playground)

paper

pencils, crayons, or markers

Investigation

1. Make tiny holes in the resealable bag and carefully place the lizard (or other creature) inside.
2. Invite the class to discuss what they know about lizards and their needs.
3. In small groups, invite students to observe the lizard. You might want to tape the edges of the bag to a tabletop. Children can still look closely without harming the lizard.
4. Encourage children to record their observations with pictures or words.
5. Invite students to share what they discovered about the characteristics of the lizard.
6. Release the lizard onto the playground. (Do not leave the lizard in the bag for over an hour.)

EXTENSIONS

- Under close supervision, students can take the lizard out of the bag to observe.
- Students can observe and compare the characteristics of several creatures found in the classroom or on the playground.

SOIL SEARCH

Children will grow and observe a microcosm in a plastic bag.

Investigation

1. Select a plot of soil that is fertile and has signs of life in it. Help each child place 1/2 cup of this soil in a resealable bag.
2. Add a small piece of leather and a sprinkle of water to each bag.
3. Help children seal the bags securely while capturing some air inside and then place the bags in a sunny location.
4. Encourage children to describe their soil with pictures or words. What do you see in your soil sample?
5. Encourage children to predict what they think they will see in their bags in three days, one week, or two weeks.
6. At appropriate intervals, encourage students to observe their bags and record their observations.
7. At the end of two weeks, children can share their observations. Invite the class to speculate how the changes took place and where the plants and animals came from. Discuss the meaning of the word *microcosm*.

MATERIALS

quart-size resealable bags

soil

leather

water

paper

pencils, markers, or crayons

EXTENSIONS

- Use soil samples from different plots.
- Place the soil samples in different environmental locations.

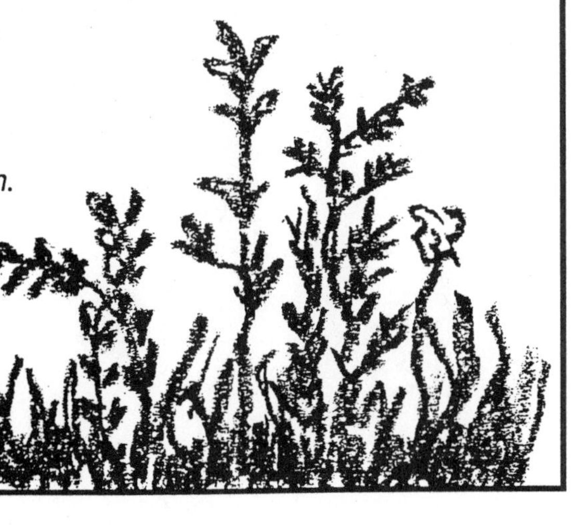

SEEDS AND SPROUTS

Children will germinate seeds in resealable bags and discuss the life cycle of a plant.

- quart-size resealable bags
- paper towels
- seeds (lima beans, peas, or corn)
- water
- liquid bleach
- paper
- pencils, markers, or crayons

Investigation

1. Soak each type of seed in separate bags of lukewarm water overnight.
2. Help each child fold and slide a paper towel into a resealable bag so that the entire bag is filled with the paper towel.
3. Add just enough water to the bag to moisten the paper towel.
4. To prevent mold in the germination bags, have children dip their seeds in a solution of 1 cup water and 2 Tbsp. bleach before placing the seeds into the bags on the moistened towels.
5. Seal the bags securely and place them in designated areas of the room.
6. Over a two-week period, invite children to observe and chart the plant growth.
7. Encourage students to share their observations. Discuss what seeds need to grow, parts of plants, and plant life cycles.

EXTENSIONS

- Staple bags to the bulletin board so that the students can compare the growth among the bags.
- Study the effects of various variables, such as position of seeds, light, and temperature, on the growth of the seeds.
- After the seeds germinate and begin to grow, plant them in small pots to encourage their continued growth.

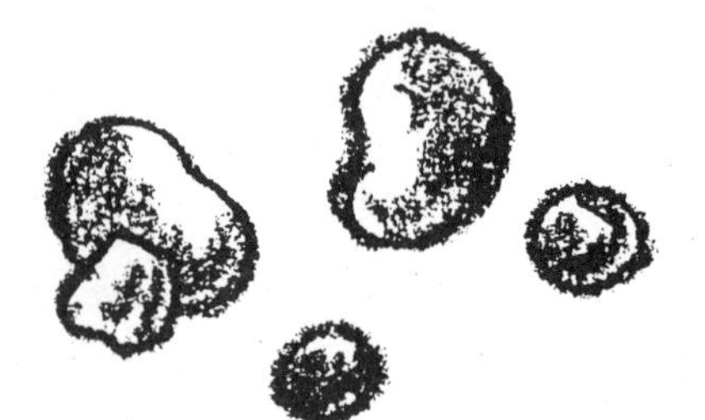

MOLDY OLDY

Children will observe mold growing on bread.

Materials

quart-size resealable bags

bread

spray bottle with water

chart paper

pencils, markers, or crayons

Investigation

1. Ask each child to bring a slice of bread from home. (Have extra slices on hand for those children who forget or are unable to bring bread.)
2. Discuss the many different types of bread and create a graph to show size, color, or favorites.
3. Invite each child to carefully sprinkle water onto his or her slice of bread, place it in a bag, and seal the bag securely.
4. Collect the bags and staple them onto a bulletin board for students to observe for two weeks. What do you think will happen to the slices of bread? Will they change? How?
5. Encourage children to observe the bread every 2 to 3 days for a two-week period. Encourage them to record their observations with pictures or words.
6. After the two-week period, ask children to share their findings with the class. What is mold? How are the molds on different slices of bread different or alike? What could you do to prevent mold from growing?

Extensions

- Prepare five bags of bread using the identical type of bread and amount of sprinkled water. Place each bag in a different location to test the effect environmental conditions have on the growth of mold.
- Experiment with mold growth on other foods or materials, such as leather, fabric, or pennies.

LET'S GET DIRTY

Children will compare and contrast soil samples and hypothesize which soil would be best for plant growth.

MATERIALS

quart-size resealable bags

plastic spoons or scoops

permanent marker

cookie sheets

Investigation

1. Give each child a resealable bag and a spoon or scoop.
2. Take children on a nature walk around the school yard, neighborhood park, or play area.
3. Invite each child to collect an individual soil sample in his or her resealable bag.
4. Using a permanent marker, label each child's bag to indicate where the soil sample was gathered.
5. After returning to the classroom, encourage children to work in groups of four or five to study their soil samples. Children can empty one bag of soil at a time onto a cookie sheet. Ask children to observe, compare, and contrast the color and texture of each sample. What was common to all soil samples? What characteristics were unique to each sample?
6. Invite children to form a hypothesis about which soil would be best for plant growth.

EXTENSIONS

- Invite children to graph the results of their soil comparisons.
- Encourage children to brainstorm other attributes of the soil samples that they could compare and contrast, such as temperature and weight.
- Weigh the four samples and encourage the children to place the bags of soil in descending order according to weight.
- If there was litter in the soil samples, encourage students to explore ways to clean up the litter.
- Invite children to design an experiment that would test their hypothesis about which soil would be best for growing plants.
- Challenge children to use the soil samples to make a soil relief map of the area from which the soil samples were taken.

ROCK SHAKE DOWN

Children will predict and test the hardness of several rocks.

MATERIALS

sandwich-size resealable freezer bags

rock samples (granite, marble, and sandstone work well)

music

paper

pencils, crayons, or markers

Investigation

1. Spark students' interest in this activity by asking them to share what they know about rocks.
2. Divide the class into small groups. Give each group a sampling of various types of rocks and give each child in the group a resealable bag.
3. Invite students to examine the rocks. Encourage children to predict and record the hardness of each sample by arranging the rocks from hardest to softest. Which rocks will break easily? Which rocks will be difficult to break?
4. Invite each child to fill his or her bag with a selection of rocks.
5. Play some lively music while children move their bodies and shake their rock bags vigorously. Encourage children to explore ways of shaking their bags using different body parts.
6. After an appropriate amount of time, examine the bags to determine which rocks are softer as evidenced by broken pieces in the bags. Invite students to record their findings with words or illustrations.
7. Compare the predictions and results.

EXTENSIONS

- Extend the activity with a discussion on erosion.
- Instead of shaking the rocks, students can test their hardness by scraping them with a coin.
- Invite children to brainstorm other ways to break the rocks into smaller pieces besides shaking the bags.

LEAF BOOKS

Children will study the structure of various leaves and display the leaves in "bag books."

MATERIALS

sandwich-size resealable bags

various types of leaves

8 1/2" x 11" paper (cut into eighths)

pencils, crayons, markers

sewing needle with large eye

dental floss

Investigation

1. Using the sewing needle and dental floss, sew together five resealable bags to make a "bag book" for each child. Sew the bag ends that are opposite of the resealable ends together to ensure that the bags can still be opened.
2. Invite children to gather various types of leaves that have fallen to the ground.
3. Compare and contrast the structure of various leaves.
4. Invite children to place a different type of leaf in each page of their "bag books."
5. Encourage children to describe each leaf on a small piece of paper. Help children place the paper inside the page with the appropriate leaf.

EXTENSIONS

- Use photographs or pictures instead of real leaves.
- Invite children to brainstorm other "bag book" topics, such as dinosaurs, foods, and colors.
- As a language development exercise, encourage children to "read" their books to you and one another. Ask children what happened first, last, and so on in their stories. What would happen if you replaced this picture with your last picture? How would your story change?

NATURE'S SURPRISES

Children will brainstorm supplies that would be needed in the event of a natural disaster and collect some of the items for their own emergency bags.

Investigation

1. Ask children to consider what items might be difficult to find and needed in the event of a natural disaster. Record their ideas on chart paper.
2. Write a letter to parents requesting their assistance with the supplies needed to build the emergency bags. Each child can sign his or her name to the letter.
3. When supplies are collected, help children place the supplies in their own resealable bags.
4. Using permanent markers, write students' names on the bags.
5. Obtain a copy of each child's emergency release form to place in each child's bag.

EXTENSIONS

- Discuss with children the natural disasters or emergencies that could occur in your local area.
- Encourage children to gather emergency supplies at home to help prepare their families for the unexpected.

MATERIALS

large resealable bags

various supplies (small juice cartons, light sticks, bandages, granola bars, dried fruit)

chart paper

permanent markers

emergency release forms

I'M A LITTLE RUSTY

Children will learn about rust and what conditions promote its formation.

MATERIALS

sandwich-size resealable bags

pieces of steel wool or nails

water

paper

pencils, markers, or crayons

Investigation

1. Invite children to share their experiences with rust. Have you ever seen rust? What does rust do? What kinds of materials rust? What causes rust?
2. Prepare the following bags.
   Bag A: steel wool in a sealed bag with as much air removed as possible
   Bag B: steel wool in an unsealed bag
   Bag C: steel wool in a sealed bag with 1/8 cup of water
   Bag D: steel wool in an unsealed bag with 1/8 cup of water

3. After displaying each bag, encourage children to predict and record what they think will happen after one week and two weeks.
4. Staple the bags to a bulletin board so the class can easily observe them.
5. Over a two-week period, encourage children to examine the bags and record their observations.
6. At the end of two weeks, invite children to share their findings. What conditions promote rust? What conditions prevent rust? What kinds of problems can rust cause?

EXTENSIONS

- **Experiment to discover what materials are more likely to rust by placing different objects in resealable bags. Be sure to place all the bags in the same location under the same conditions.**
- **Experiment to discover other factors, such as temperature and light, that might have an effect on the formation of rust.**

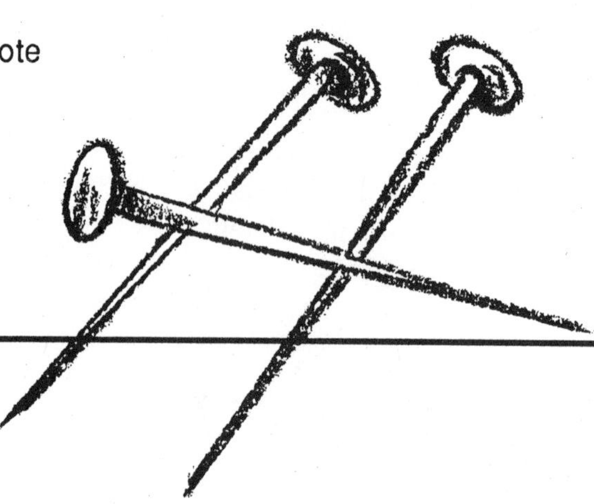

FLOWERS FOR KEEPS

Children will study the parts of flowers and then dry some flowers.

MATERIALS

sandwich-size resealable bags

cut flowers

baking soda

paper

pencils, markers, or crayons

Investigation

1. Invite each child to select a flower and write or draw a description of it. What words describe your flower?
2. Help each child place his or her flower in a bag and cover it with baking soda before sealing the bag.
3. Place the flowers in a dark place for about a week.
4. Ask children to predict what they think will happen. What words do you think will describe your flower in one week? How might your flower look different than it did before you placed it in the bag?
5. After one week, invite children to observe and describe their flowers with words or pictures. How is your flower different? How is your flower the same?

EXTENSIONS

- **Place the resealable bags in various locations, such as a lighted area, cooler area, or warmer area.**
- **Use different types of flowers.**

THIRSTY FLOWERS

Children will learn about osmosis by observing colored water travel up the stem of a flower.

MATERIALS

large resealable bags

cut flowers (preferably ones that are light in color)

water

tape

food coloring

paper

stapler

pencils, markers, or crayons

scissors

Investigation

1. Ask children to predict what they think will happen to a flower if the stem is soaking in colored water.
2. Give each child a flower with the bottom of the stem cut at a diagonal. Help children tape the flower to the inside of a resealable bag.
3. Have children mix 1/4 cup water with a few drops of food coloring and pour it into the resealable bag.
4. Seal the bags and staple them to the bulletin board.

5. Encourage children to observe any changes that take place for a one-week period. Encourage them to record their observations with pictures or words.
6. Invite the class to share their observations. Discuss cellular osmosis.

EXTENSIONS

- Test variables that may affect the outcome, such as location, temperature, and light.
- Use different types of flowers and investigate any differences in the rate of cellular osmosis.
- Examine the parts of a flower.

GRAB BAG

Children will collect items, such as soil, leaves, and trash, while on a nature walk and then compare and contrast what they gathered.

Investigation

1. Give each child a quart-size resealable bag with his or her name printed on it and a sandwich-size bag.
2. Discuss with the class the types of objects you would like them to collect as you go on a class nature walk.
3. Show children how to use the sandwich-size bag as a glove to pick up objects and place them in the larger bag.
4. After returning to the classroom, invite children to work in small groups as they empty their bags and compare and contrast what they have gathered. (You might want to cover the work area with newspaper.)
5. After an appropriate amount of time each group may write a description or make an illustration of their findings.

EXTENSIONS

- Students may make a collage using the items they collected.
- Instead of going on a nature walk at school, students can collect items as a homework assignment.

MATERIALS

quart-size resealable bags

sandwich-size resealable bags

permanent markers

paper

pencils or crayons

newspaper

TOOTH TEST

Children will learn about tooth decay by observing the effects of cola, water, and mouthwash on real teeth.

MATERIALS

sandwich-size resealable bags

real teeth (or egg shells)

paper

cola

water

mouthwash

paper

pencils, markers, or crayons

Investigation

1. Lead children in a discussion about tooth decay. What foods do you think are more likely to cause cavities? What foods are less likely to cause cavities?
2. Place one tooth in a bag filled with mouthwash, one in a bag filled with water, and one in a bag filled with cola.
3. Invite students to record their observations every 2-3 days.
4. After two weeks, examine the teeth. Invite children to record and discuss their observations.
5. Discuss what causes tooth decay and ways to prevent it. Substances containing sugar promote the growth of bacteria on teeth. Bacteria causes tooth decay.

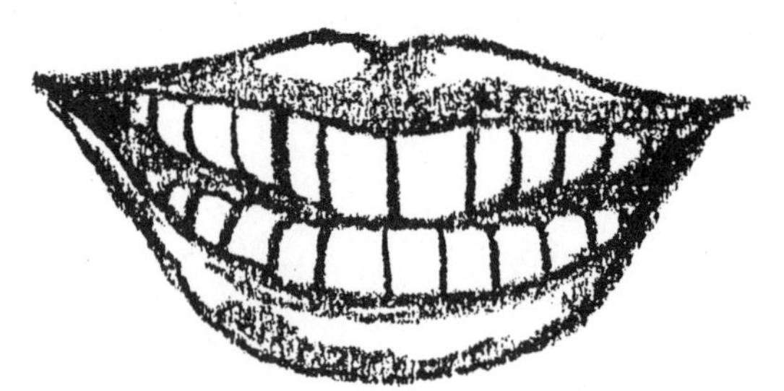

EXTENSIONS

- Children may want to use their own primary teeth when they fall out for a similar experiment.
- Try using other liquids, such as vinegar and sugar water.
- If real teeth are unavailable, egg shells make a good substitute. With egg shells, the experiment can be completed in one day.

SMILES THAT SPARKLE

Children will discover the ingredients in tooth powder and make some of their own.

sandwich-size resealable bags

baking soda

table salt

flavorings, such as peppermint extract

plastic spoons

paper cups

Investigation

1. Place each powdered material in separate labeled paper cups.
2. Discuss the importance of good dental hygiene.
3. Invite each child to create some unique tooth powder by combining 4 teaspoons baking soda, 1 teaspoon salt, and 3 drops of flavoring in a resealable bag.
4. Have children seal the bags securely before mixing the ingredients.
5. When children take the tooth powder home, invite them to rub it on their teeth.
6. Discuss how the tooth powder is different from toothpaste.

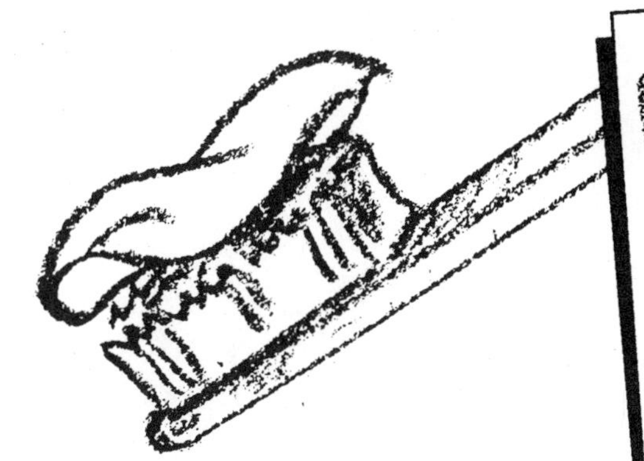

EXTENSIONS

- Children can make larger batches of the tooth powder and invite friends and family members to try it.
- Invite children to conduct a survey on favorite types of toothpaste or powder. Encourage children to record their results and share them with the class.

YOU GOTTA HAVE BACKBONE

Children will test the effect of vinegar on bones and discuss what bones need to be strong and healthy.

MATERIALS

quart-size resealable bags

dry chicken bones (legs work best)

vinegar

paper

pencils, markers, or crayons

Investigation

1. Ask children what they think bones need to grow strong and healthy and what happens when bones do not get what they need.
2. Place one chicken bone in a bag. Place another bone in a bag with 1/2 cup vinegar.
3. Invite children to predict and record what will happen to the two bones after one week.
4. Place the bags in a location that is easily accessible. Encourage children to daily observe the bones and record their findings with pictures or words.
5. At the end of one week, invite students to share results. In what ways are the two bones different? How are the bones still alike? How easily does each bone bend? (The bone in the vinegar will be soft because vinegar is a weak acid and breaks down the calcium that makes bones strong.)
6. Discuss that bones need minerals, such as calcium and phosphorus, to grow and be strong.

EXTENSIONS

- Experiment to see what other ingredients act as a weak acid on bones.
- Discuss what foods (rich in the minerals) are needed to grow strong bones.

CLEAN HANDS

Children will observe the effects of not cleaning their hands.

MATERIALS

resealable bags

4 potatoes (peeled and stored in a bag)

soil

large bowls

hand soap

warm water

cold water

paper towels

Investigation

1. Peel and wash the potatoes. Store them is a sealed bag until ready to use.
2. Discuss the importance of cleanliness.
3. Invite four children to dirty their hands in the soil.
4. Have one of those four children rub his or her hands on a potato and place the potato in a separate resealable bag. Seal and label the bag.
5. Have the remaining three students wash their hands as follows:
   warm water only
   cold water and soap
   warm water and soap
6. Have each of the three students rub their hands on separate potatoes and seal the potatoes in labeled bags.
7. Encourage children to predict what will happen. After five days, examine the bags.
8. Discuss the results of the investigation as well as the importance of keeping hands clean.

EXTENSIONS

- Try the investigation again using different brands of soap.
- Invite children to keep a record of how many times a day they wash their hands.

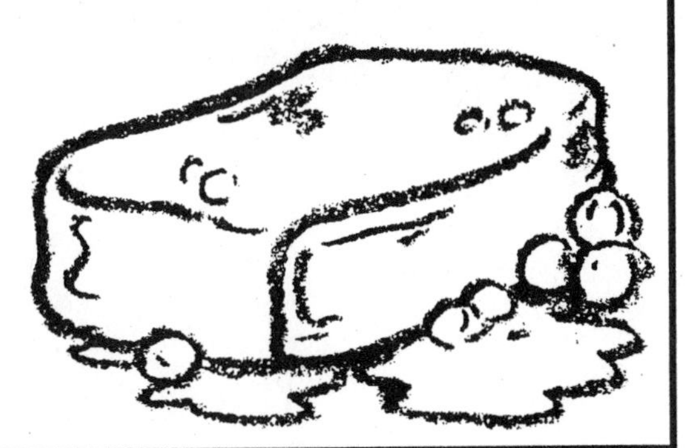

WHAT DRAWS ME TO YOU

Children will examine, predict, test, and classify a variety of magnetic and non-magnetic objects.

Investigation

1. Place each object in a resealable bag, seal securely, and staple or tape to a bulletin board.
2. Tie a magnet to a string (long enough to reach every bag) and attach it to the bulletin board.
3. Invite children to predict which objects will be attracted to the magnet. Record their predictions. What does a magnet do? What materials are attracted to magnets? What materials are not attracted to magnets?
4. Have children take turns passing the magnet over the bags and observing what happens.
5. Encourage children to record their findings with pictures or words.
6. Compare children's results to their predictions. What conclusions can you make about magnets?

sandwich-size resealable bags

magnets

string

objects (aluminum foil, nails, safety pins, cork, paper, paper clips, screws, copper wiring, plastic, scissors, wood)

chart paper

markers

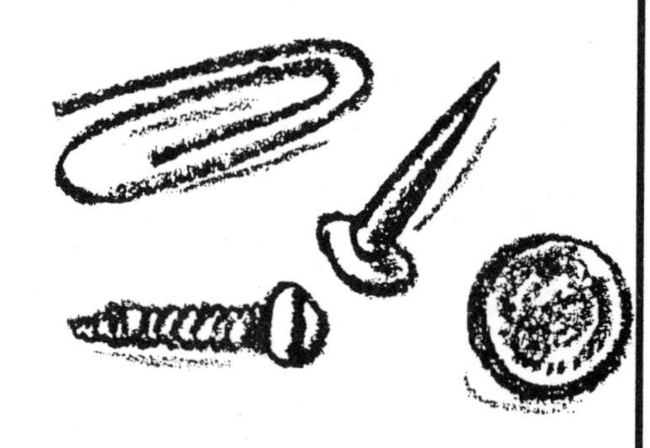

EXTENSIONS

- Invite children to bring objects from home to be included in the activity.
- Use different shapes or strengths of magnets.

ABSOLUTELY ATTRACTIVE

Children will examine, predict, test, and classify a variety of magnetic and non-magnetic objects.

MATERIALS

sandwich-size resealable bags

bar magnets

brass, iron, and aluminum screws

iron and brass nails

copper and steel wire

steel and brass pins

bronze and nickel coins

chart paper

markers

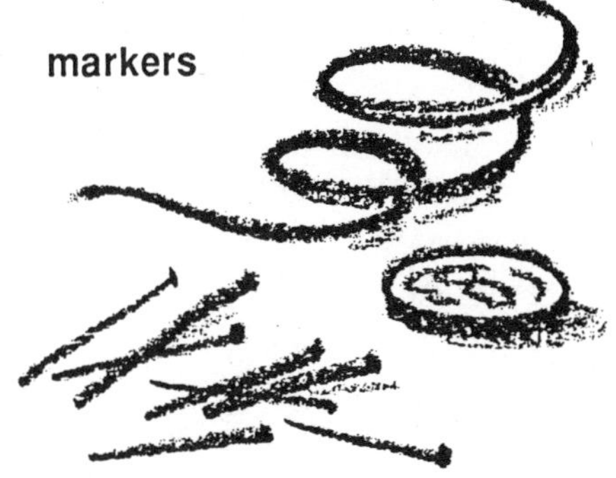

Investigation

1. Prepare and label the following five bags.
   Bag A: brass, iron, and aluminum screws
   Bag B: iron nails and brass nails
   Bag C: copper and steel wire
   Bag D: steel and brass pins
   Bag E: bronze and nickel coins
2. Display the bags for children to view. Compare and contrast the contents in each bag.
3. Encourage children to predict which objects will be attracted to a magnet and record their predictions on chart paper.
4. Invite children to move magnets through and around the contents of each bag. Observe what happens and record the results next to the predictions.
5. Encourage children to draw conclusions about materials that are attracted to magnets.

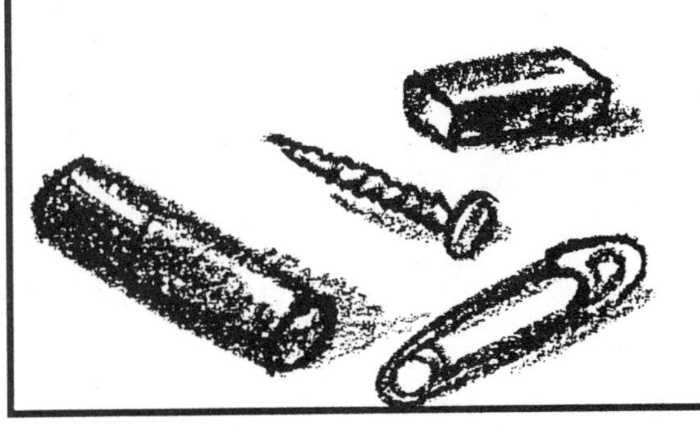

EXTENSIONS

- **Invite children to design additional experiments. How can we discover if an item is made of steel, brass, iron, copper, aluminum, nickel, or bronze if it is painted?**
- **Use different shapes or strengths of magnets.**

STATIC ELECTRICITY

Children will predict and observe the properties of static electricity.

MATERIALS

gallon-size resealable bags

Styrofoam packing pieces (the pieces that look like peanuts work great)

piece of wool fabric

Investigation

1. Invite each child to place a handful of Styrofoam pieces into a resealable bag.
2. Help children inflate the bags as much as possible before sealing securely.
3. Ask children to predict what would happen if they rub a piece of wool on their inflated bags.
4. Invite children to test their hypotheses. Encourage them to experiment by rubbing their bags on their clothing or on their hair.
5. Discuss the observations and encourage children to draw conclusions. What is static electricity? (Friction causes electrons to move from the wool to the bag. This creates a temporary negative charge in the bag and a positive charge in the wool.)

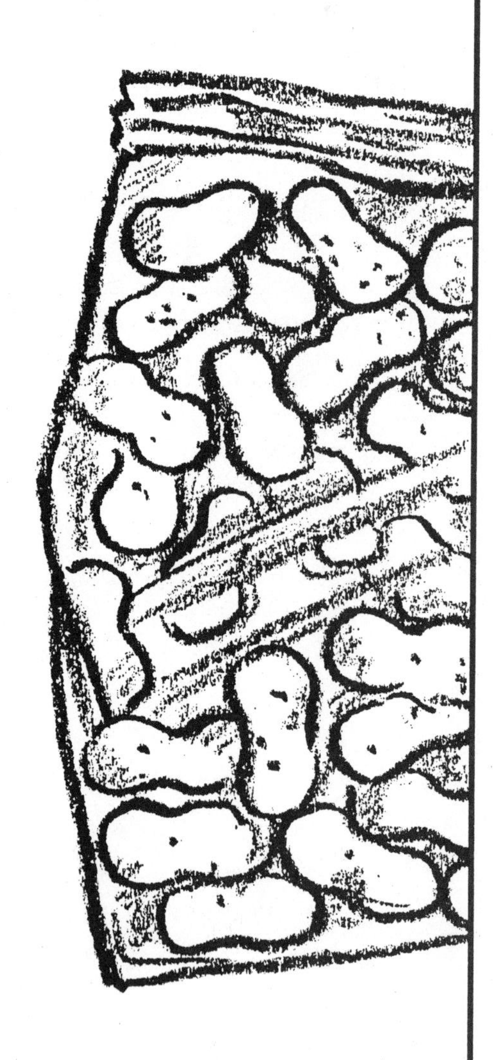

EXTENSIONS

- Make static electricity bags using different materials, such as puffed rice cereal, small pieces of paper, paper clips, or cottonballs. Encourage children to predict and test whether an electric charge exists between the wool and each object.
- Perform the same investigation using a plastic wand and a balloon.

AIR BAGS

Children will discover that air has volume and can do work.

MATERIALS

quart-size resealable bags

drinking straws

books

paper

pencils, markers, or crayons

Investigation

1. Invite students to share what they know about the properties of air. Is air real? How can you tell if you cannot see it?
2. Help each child insert a straw in a bag and zip the bag closed as much as possible.
3. Ask children to blow air into their bags and record their observations.
4. Have children deflate their bags and place them on their desks and then place a book on top of their deflated bags.
5. Ask children to once again blow into the straw to fill their bags with air. Encourage children to record what happens.
6. Invite students to share their findings and lead a discussion on the properties of air.

EXTENSIONS

- Try the experiment using different-sized objects and resealable bags.
- Blow up several bags and seal them tightly. Invite children to toss them in the air and throw them back and forth to one another. Experiment and compare tossing bags with and without air as well as bags with objects inside.

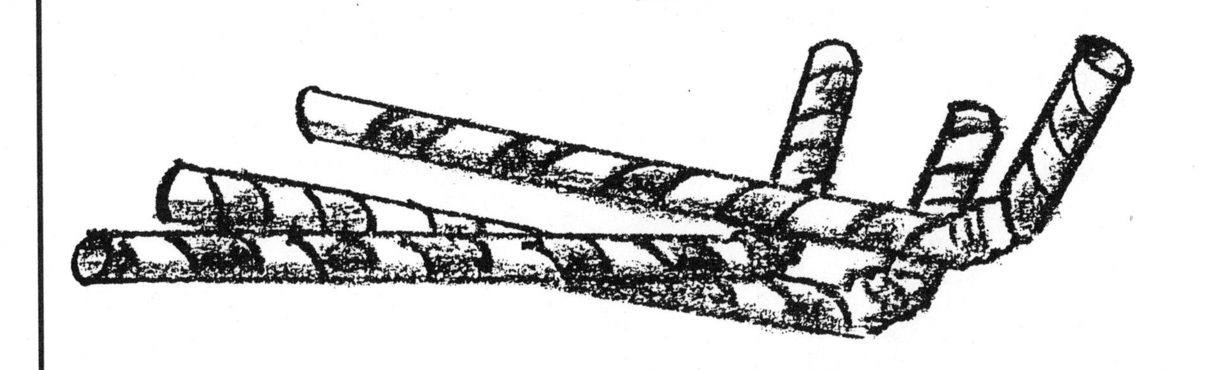

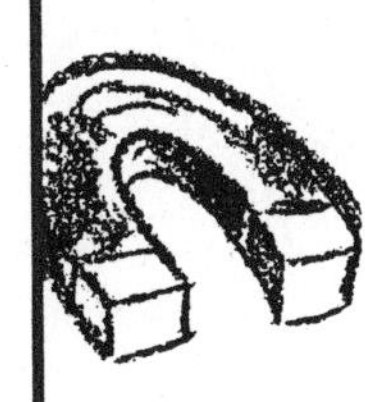

GRAVITY AND GRAVY

Children will discuss the effects of gravity and explore what it would be like to eat in space.

MATERIALS

sandwich-size resealable bags

drinking straws

applesauce

spoons

Investigation

1. Discuss gravity and its effects. What does gravity do? How would your life be different without gravity?
2. Encourage students to speculate what would happen if astronauts in space tried to eat their food off a plate the way we do. How can astronauts solve the problem of their food floating away? How could we test your ideas?
3. Help each child spoon some applesauce into a resealable bag, add a straw, and seal as tightly as possible.
4. Encourage students to "eat" their applesauce like the astronauts by sucking it through their straws.

EXTENSIONS

- Substitute different foods, such as pudding, oatmeal, or soup.
- Instead of using a straw, zip the bag completely. Then cut a small opening by snipping off one corner of the lower bag. Children can suck the contents out of the bag through the corner hole.

FEELING FOOD

Children will observe, describe, and group various foods according to texture.

Investigation

1. Partially fill each resealable bag with a different textured food and seal securely.
2. Discuss vocabulary for different textures, such as rough, smooth, and sticky. Provide examples if necessary. As a class, brainstorm words to describe the textures of the foods. (With young children, you might want to limit the list to five words.)
3. Invite children to write the five words as headings on a sheet of paper.
4. Encourage children to work in groups to sort the foods according to texture. Help children record each food under the correct heading using pictures or words.
5. After an appropriate amount of time, encourage the class to share their findings. Which bags could you identify the contents by using the sense of touch only? Do any of the bags feel the same? How could you change the feel of some of the bags?

MATERIALS

sandwich-size resealable bags

crackers

spaghetti (different sizes and shapes)

chips

cereal (several different kinds)

rice

sugar

salt

oil

fruit juice

honey

flour

peanut butter

raisins

shortening

paper

pencils, crayons, or markers

EXTENSIONS

- Invite children to sequence the bags from softest to hardest.
- Ask each child to bring one food item from home to fill the bags for the investigation. This will add to the variety of textures as well as make a home-school connection.
- Challenge children to identify what is in each bag while blindfolded.
- Fill the texture bags with objects rather than food.

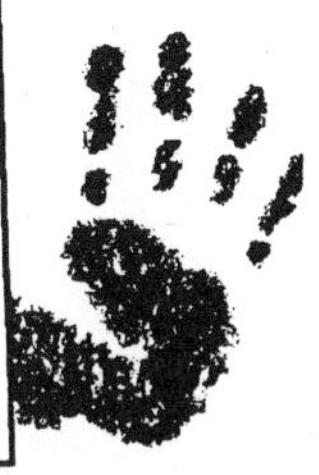

TEXTURE BOOKS

Children will create texture books.

Investigation

1. Using the sewing needle and dental floss, sew together five resealable bags to make a "bag book" for each child. Sew the bag sides together to ensure that the bags can still be opened.
2. Brainstorm with the class words to describe textures. Invite children to write the words on separate small slips of paper.
3. Encourage students to place each slip of paper in a separate page of their "bag books."
4. Invite children to place a different textured object in each page to match the descriptive words.
5. After an appropriate amount of time, encourage the class to share their books.

MATERIALS

sandwich-size resealable bags

various textured objects (sand paper, cotton balls, fabric swatches)

8 1/2" x 11" paper (cut into eighths)

sewing needle with large eye

dental floss

pencils, crayons, or markers

EXTENSIONS

- Use photographs or pictures cut from magazines instead of real objects.
- Encourage students to bring textured materials from home.
- Use other topics, such as dinosaurs, foods, and colors, to make other "bag books."

SQUISHY, SQUISHY BAGS

Children will identify and compare cooked and uncooked foods.

Investigation

1. Discuss children's prior knowledge with the selected foods, including how each feels, smells, and looks when cooked and uncooked.
2. Place each cooked and uncooked food in separate resealable bags.
3. Invite children to feel and smell the bags without a blindfold.
4. Have children predict if they will be able to identify each food without their sense of sight.
5. Encourage each child to feel and smell the bags while wearing a blindfold. Record each child's identification of each bag.
6. Encourage children to compare their identification of each bag to what is actually inside and to discuss their sensory experiences with one another. Which of these bags did not feel squishy? What are some other things that would feel squishy if you touched them? What other parts of your body could you use to touch the squishy bags?

MATERIALS

sandwich-size resealable bags

several foods both cooked and uncooked (spaghetti, rice, oatmeal or grits, potatoes)

blindfold

paper

EXTENSIONS

- Prepare two identical bags for each ingredient. Invite children to pair the matching bags using only their sense of touch.
- While blindfolded, children can match an uncooked food to its cooked counterpart.

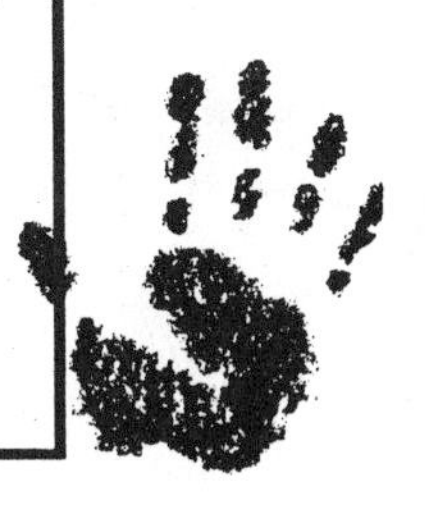

GOO BAGS

Children will investigate the properties of "goo."

Investigation

1. Invite students to help you prepare "goo" by combining 1 cup cornstarch, 1/3 cup sugar, and 4 cups of water. Stir over medium heat until the mixture thickens. Cool completely.
2. Divide "goo" into three large resealable bags. Add food coloring (one primary color to each bag) and seal securely.
3. Have children mix the colors into the "goo" by massaging and manipulating the sealed bags.
4. Spoon the "goo" into the mixing bowls.
5. Invite each child to spoon some "goo" into his or her own resealable bag. Children can choose which colors they would like to mix.
6. Encourage children to manipulate their sealed bags of "goo" to experiment with mixing colors. What color of "goo" is in your bag? How could you make that color darker or lighter?

MATERIALS

quart-size resealable bags

three mixing bowls

cooking pan

hot plate (adult use only)

cornstarch

sugar

water

food coloring (primary colors)

spoons

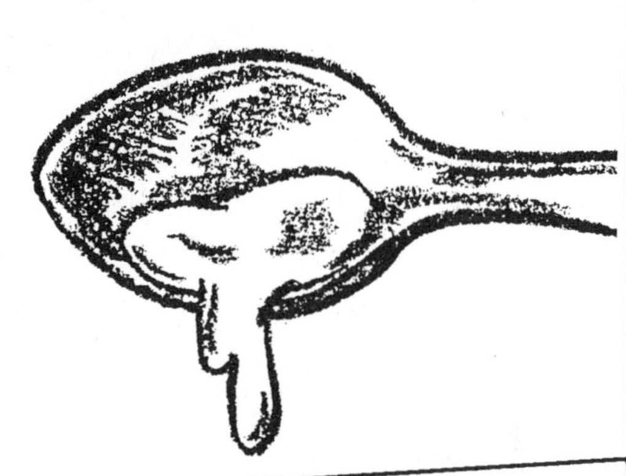

EXTENSIONS

- Children can create other experiments with their "goo" bags. What will happen if you place your "goo" bag in a refrigerator overnight?
- Read *Bartholomew and the Oobleck* by Dr. Seuss.

MAGIC SLATES

Children will draw on "magic slates" and consider why the materials used to make the slates are effective.

MATERIALS

large resealable freezer bags

catsup

masking tape

cookie sheets

Investigation

1. Place approximately 1/2 cup of catsup in each resealable bag. Release as much air from the bags as possible. Seal securely and tape the closure for added protection.
2. Tape all edges of each bag to a cookie sheet or desk top so the bags are taut and securely fixed in place.
3. Invite children to use their fingers to write or draw on the bag. What does it feel like when you draw on the bag? How can you erase your writing?
4. After an appropriate amount of time, encourage children to share their observations. Discuss the properties of catsup that might make it especially effective to make magic slates. What other substances could you place in a bag to make a magic slate? What substances would not work well for this activity? Why?

EXTENSIONS

- Use several slates simultaneously at a learning center.
- Make slates using substances, such as pudding, shaving cream, or mustard.

FINGER PAINTING FUN

Children will investigate the properties of finger paint and create their own designs.

MATERIALS

sandwich-size resealable bags

powdered laundry starch

bowl

cold water

boiling water

1/2 cup soap flakes

food coloring

finger paint paper

hot plate (adult use only)

Investigation

1. Place 1 cup laundry starch in a bowl and add enough cold water to form a paste.
2. Add 5 cups of boiling water to the paste and cook over low heat until smooth and shiny.
3. Add soap flakes and food coloring.
4. Place different colors of finger paint in separate resealable bags.
5. Invite children to dip their fingers in the paint to feel, smell, and observe it. How does it feel? What does it smell like? What other things feel the same as finger paint?
6. Children can create designs on finger paint paper.

EXTENSIONS

- Add sand, sawdust, glycerin, or other substances to the finger paint to provide more tactile experiences as children manipulate the securely sealed bags.

MUD PAINT

Children will make and observe the properties of mud paint.

MATERIALS

sandwich-size resealable bags

potting soil

newsprint or construction paper

water-based paint in small containers

spoons

newspaper

Investigation

1. Help each child place about one cup of potting soil in a resealable bag.
2. Invite each child to choose a color of paint to add to the bag of soil.
3. Encourage children to predict what they think the soil and paint mixture will look and feel like. Invite them to discuss if they think the mixture will make a good paint.
4. Help children add the paint to the soil and then securely seal their bags. (They may need to add a little water to the soil and paint to get a consistency usable for painting.)
5. As children manipulate the paint and soil in the sealed bags, encourage them to observe and discuss their thoughts.
6. Provide newsprint for children to use for painting pictures using the mud paint. Invite children to use their fingers as brushes.
7. When students have completed their designs, encourage them to share their observations and what they liked or disliked about the mud-paint mixture. How is this paint different from other paint you have used? What else would you like to try to add to the paint?

EXTENSIONS

- Read "The Dirtiest Man in the World" from *Where the Sidewalk Ends* by Shel Silverstein.
- Use other substances, such as sawdust, sand, or blueberries to make paints.

SCULPTURES

Students will investigate the properties of Plaster of Paris and create their own sculptures.

MATERIALS

quart-size resealable bags

Plaster of Paris

water

newspaper

Investigation

1. Place a small portion of ready-to-mold Plaster of Paris inside a resealable bag for each child. Release most of the air from the bags and seal securely.
2. Encourage children to observe and describe the dry plaster.
3. Invite children to add a small amount of water to the plaster and securely reseal their bags. (Cover work areas with newspaper for easy cleanup.)
4. Encourage children to mold the plaster into a sculpture by massaging and manipulating the bag.
5. After the sculptures have hardened, help children remove them from the bags. (The plaster will harden in a few minutes.)
6. Encourage children to observe the properties of the plaster.
7. Invite children to compare the properties of the plaster before and after the addition of water.

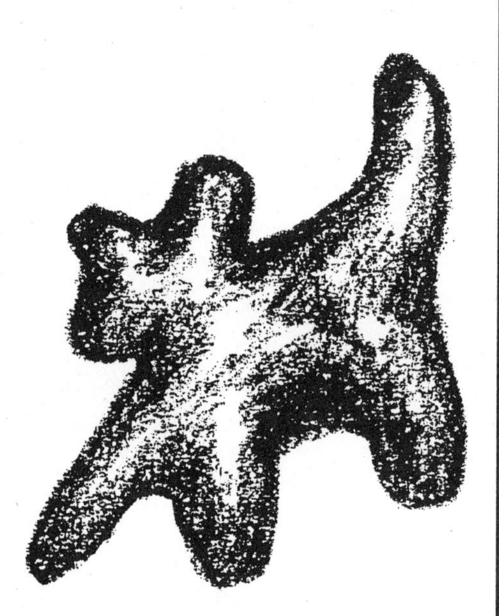

EXTENSIONS

- Add food coloring to the Plaster of Paris.
- Students may want to paint their hardened sculptures.
- Invite children to name their sculptures and set up a museum for other students to tour.